JIM SHELLI

CW00346187

Magic of the Midlands and the Black Country

'Strictly Vintage and In Tune'

For Grown-up Kids of all ages

First published in Great Britain in 2001 by The Black Country Society.

ISBN 0 904015 63 7

To order more copies of this book please contact Minimag Co. 358 Birmingham Road, Walsall WS5 3NX.

Printed in Great Britain by Action Print & Design Ltd.
Building 12, The Pensnett Estate, Kingswinford, West Midlands DY6 7PP.

Cover design by The Charles Group
Hampshire House, High Street, Kingswinford, West Midlands DY6 8AW.

Contents

FOREWORD

In this book, compiled by Jim Shelley, are mentioned a number of the finest and innovative engineering characters ever to come out of the Black Country and the Midlands. All into the 'Golden Age' of the motor cycle, the car and aircraft development, as well as a myriad of other mechanical items fashioned out of various metals.

We have had the privilege to have seen the greatest developments unfold in our day and age than in any other in the history of mankind.

The Black Country and the Midlands has added enormously to these developments, always at the forefront of engineering knowledge, from the back shed to the great works. It is true to say that the Black Country and Midland engineers are a fine race of people regardless of whether they are on the shop floor or in design and management. They have produced an infinite amount of useful items enhancing the life of mankind all over the world.

We hope that you will enjoy this book about some of the good work done over the years by the characters mentioned. As in the Holy Bible 'In the beginning was the word'. This has always been recognised by the Black Country man 'Ommer it and Shaerp it!'

Whilst, in the south-east, people with time on their hands are dreaming up white elephants like the Millennium Dome, Paul Morgan is making Formula One winning engines, Len Vale-Onslow (100 years old) is filing in his workshop, Barry Hares is making his magnificent 24 cylinder sleeve valve Rolls Royce Eagle, and numerous model engineers in their sheds are creating masterpieces.

We hope that you will get as much pleasure in reading this book as it has given Jim in compiling it, and will give you an insight into the Black Country and Midland engineers in general.

Richard Barnes.

Richard Barnes pictured with his Miles Messenger at St Just in Cornwall.
Richard, an ex Black countryman from Walsall, local historian and pilot who now lives in Lamorna, Cornwall, surrounded by a 12-50 Alvis Beetleback, a Mk VI Bentley, and high-speed dogs based on greyhounds crossed with Staffordshire Bull Terriers that run like hell and can't half bite!. He produces historic Black Country tapes under the pseudonym 'Arf a Mo'.

A NOTE FROM THE AUTHOR

It may appear at first glance that this book covers a large variety of unrelated subjects. However, on closer scrutiny it will be found that they bear an amazing resemblance to each other in so far that approach, irrespective of the subject and inspiration, is required in each category.

The final results do not always come out as originally intended, but every now and again, due to intermediate events, come out surprisingly better than expected. As an example slavishly trying to emulate Louis Armstrong will make you one of many 'not quite as good'. Alternatively, inadvertently bunging a D7 into Ole Miss Rag, or moving a magneto rotor 10 degrees will sometimes improve things.

i.e. *Musically,* to enhance the harmony of a tune,

Electro-magnetically increases the flux to make all the little red veins stand out in the eyeballs when you grab the H.T. lead.

Criticism and discouragement, far from stopping progress, can inspire increased effort. This applies to Engineering, Flying, Designing, Improving technique, or Overcoming a wave of apathy on completing a number. Next time it can be a standing ovation.

If you bought the book for one particular interest please turn the page and the scales may be removed from your eyes, start shouting 'Hey, hey' and keep turning the pages.

Remember the first thing you try is rarely the one that you are best at and almost certainly should not exclude all others. There are the 'Talkers' and the 'Doers'. The former are mainly situated in the South-East, whereas the latter are from the remainder of the country focussing on the Midlands and Black Country areas.

Workshop of the world.

The Midlands and the Black Country undoubtedly earned this title. In this book I have only included people I have known personally but here are a few of the world-famous midland manufacturers of cars, motor cycles and engines:

Birmingham: Austin, Norton, BSA, Ariel, New Imperial, Velocette, Excelsior, Hercules, James, SOS, and even Scott moved here from Yorkshire in 1946.

Wolverhampton: Guy, Star, Sunbeam, AJS, Villiers engines (used in many makes of motor cycles), and Henry Meadows who not only made car engines (Lagonda, Frazer Nash, Invicta etc.) but also supplied commercial vehicles and motor torpedo boats in the war.

Coventry: Alvis, Jaguar, Humber, Hillman, Daimler, Lea Francis, Coventry Climax, Armstrong Siddeley, Rover, Lanchester, Riley, Singer, Standard, Talbot, and Rudge and Triumph motor cycles.

Just a few of the great midland's machines, not forgetting R.J.Mitchell's Spitfire, Frank Whittle's jet engine, and Alex Isigoni's Mini.

The Midlands Model Engineering exhibition is held each year at Castle Donnington and organised by 'Engineering in Miniature'. This brings together the cream of the country's engineers who can study each others ideas, innovations, inventions and designs and indulge in intellectual discussion.

Compare this with the south-east where the M.E. exhibition at Olympia has deteriorated into a toy show with some model engineering exhibits.

It is no surprise that 'Tate Britain' on London's Mill Bank hosts the 'Turner Prize' exhibition. This comprises of piles of junk, unmade beds, a man urinating on a chair, and the climax of this millennium fiasco, winning the £20,000 first prize, was a cold cup of coffee.

May be it is something in the air, but let's hope it is not contagious and doesn't spread up to the Midlands and Black Country.

Hopefully this book will inspire you to turn away from your computer or tele – pick up a musical instrument – and see what comes out, learn a tune, build an aeroplane – fly it, make a yacht – sail it, get a small lathe – make something, and generally become a 'Doer' and 'All round Good Egg'.

You may well then, like the author, become known as 'Lucky Jim' or possibly a 'Smart Arse'- it's up to you!   You will definitely be up and at it earlier in the morning.

THE ENGINEERS

Dedicated to GERALD SMITH – one of the Midland's great engineers.

Gerald, pictured with his own design 18 cylinder radial engine which won the Model Engineer Cup outright in 1930 being entirely built on a treadle lathe.

GERALD SMITH

Before hostilities broke out the MD of Hawker was walking down the corridor with Sidney Camm, designer of the Hurricane, when they met Gerald coming in the opposite direction.

MD: 'What do you think of the Hurricane, Gerald?'

GS: 'A very nice aeroplane. The undercarriage will collapse as soon as it hits the ground but apart from that it's OK'.

SC: 'You'd better design it then'.

He did! Followed by the undercarriages for the Manchester and Lancaster bombers none of which dared to collapse having been designed by the master.

In addition to Gerald's full size engineering achievements he manufactured model petrol engines after the war. The 7.5cc Redwing, the 10cc Lapwing, and the 15cc Magpie were all produced for resale. After a lapse of a few years and meeting me and Bill Daniel he decided to make a magneto ignition 10cc Skylark engine (pictured above). Fourteen of these beautifully made engines were sold and are now collectors' pieces. Unlike most Midland's engineers Gerald did not suffer from excessive

shyness. Comparing the Skylark to the Mona Lisa he said 'Leonardo da Vinci did the one, I've done the fourteen'.

Gerald also designed the 3 cylinder radial Osprey engine and the 5 cylinder Buzzard replicated by Bill Linfield and George Bradbury later in this book. He made his own magnetos, one of which he fitted to an OS60 for me. I was so impressed with the performance that I decided to make miniature magnetos. Gerald condemned the idea as the worst thing I could possibly do but later, on nearing completion of his 7 cylinder radial, rang up and said he didn't intend to make a magneto and proposed to use one of mine. Praise indeed!

Gerald holding my T-Beam which is powered by one of his original production 10cc Lapwing petrol engines with Coil ignition. To take this photograph I interrupted him during a casting session making Skylark Crankcases.

BARRY HARES

Before Gerald Smith died in 1990 he was fascinated by Barry Hares' magnificent one fifth scale Merlin engine, the tiny functional magnetos, variable pitch three blade prop, supercharger and incredible attention to detail.

He nearly jumped out of his skin when Barry started it up at Walsall airport on vintage day and could not be separated from the engine for the entire day.

Seventy years ago Gerald's 18 cylinder radial won the Model Engineer Cup outright and was completely built on a treadle lathe.

How much more so would Gerald have been fascinated by Barry's latest masterpiece at the Midlands Model Engineering Exhibition 2000 at Castle Donnington the Rolls Royce Eagle.

The 24 cylinder, sleeve valve, horizontally opposed **ROLLS ROYCE EAGLE** with twin crankshafts turning two four-blade contra-rotating, variable pitch props. The engine was viewed in silent awe and admiration by experienced lifelong engineers. Absolute perfection!

Not yet quite completed but Barry's incredible dedication, skill and patience reconfirm the Midlands as undoubtedly the engineering capital of the world.

MIDLANDS MODEL ENGINEERING EXHIBITION 2000

Brian Perkins' 9 cylinder sleeve valve radial on left, and on the right, flanking my Maltese Falcon, is another Perkins radial sleeve valve engine under construction. Mounted above the Maltese Falcon is my laminated 36" dia.x 24" pitch prop. The engine was awarded a 'Very Highly Commended'. A flat-four and water-cooled boat engine are shown in the foreground.

Picture shows Brian Perkins, Barry Hares and myself at Castle Donnington. It is fitting that Barry Hares should be selected as a judge of the exhibits entered by ordinary humans. The proximity of Brian and myself to Barry may possibly be due to his exalted position.

The exhibition is an annual event organised by 'Engineering in Miniature' and is now recognised as the finest model engineering exhibition in the country.

Eric Whittle, pictured right, won the 1999 Class 8 first prize with his beautiful miniature V8 engine. Neil Tidey, holding the engine, is the designer and manufacturer of Laser Four Stroke engines. Not only is the Laser the finest British Four Stroke engine but has also proved very satisfactory running on spark ignition with a Minimag magneto. Many of these are in regular use, and running on petrol, give extreme economy.

N.B. I would like to thank Neil for his help on the design of the Maltese Falcon camshaft.

GORDON WILLIAMS
Prolific model engine builder from Aldridge, near Walsall

Left: Gordon's V8 Engine, this is his own design. Note the Minimag Spark Plugs, twin carbs and exposed valve gear.

Right: Gordon's magnificent 9 Cylinder air cooled radial aero engine.

Left: Gordon's accurate scale De Haviland Gypsy engine.

Right: Unlike many model engine builders Gordon's were functional and were used in model aircraft. Pictured: One of Gordon's home built 'Mayfly' four stroke petrol engines which easily flies his 8 foot Sportster.

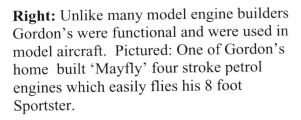

BILL LINFIELD

Bill with his 3 cylinder radial Gerald Smith 'Osprey'.

Bill with his 5 cylinder radial Gerald Smith 'Buzzard'.

Bill Linfield, a lifelong model engineer originally specialised in locomotives and stationary steam engines. He later was fascinated by Gerald Smiths drawings of a 3 cylinder Osprey internal combustion engine which was published in 'Engineering in Miniature'. He soon became expert in building four stroke petrol engines all of which had spark ignition which prompted my first encounter with him. Initially he ordered Spark Demon HT Coils for use with battery and continued to make magnificent magnetos. It is interesting that the original Gerald Smith engines had a Westbury magneto but the Minimags were smaller. This was no problem to Bill who built the engine 7/8 size.

The 'Lil Brother gas engine equipped with 'Spark Demon' and Minimag Sparkplug running on display.

Bill's replica 3 cylinder Anzani engine. As used in Bleriot's monoplane.

"Red Wing" Hit & Miss stationary engine. 1¼ inch bore, 2 inch Stroke and 8¼ inch Flywheels.

A Linfield magneto.

Bill's replica Gerald Smith Osprey.

Magneto and distributor on the 'Buzzard'.

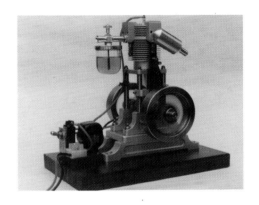

Small Hit & Miss engine.

A libation at a Cotswold pub with George Bradbury, Bill Daniel (Golden Era Kits), and Bill Linfield.

Gerald Smith looks incredulously at the superb job Bill has made of his Osprey design. Both the 3 cylinder Osprey and 5 cylinder Buzzard incorporated a unique induction system up the push-rod tubes into the sealed valve gear cover and so into the cylinder thus excluding external induction tubes.

GEORGE BRADBURY

George with his beautifully made loco has occasional 'open days' at Railway Cottages, Kings Bromley, and the local children are given rides round his garden track. On right George shows his magnificent five cylinder radial 'Gerald Smith' Buzzard.

Above: George demonstrates the Buzzard to me and Gordon Williams. He has also built a flat-four horizontally opposed aero engine and helped in the design of the Maltese Falcon.

Another prize-winning exhibit is this steam traction unit from George.

BRIAN MORGAN

Brian Morgan showed an interest in engineering from a young age and finished his education at Birmingham university gaining a B.Sc. in mechanical engineering.

After serving in the R.A.F. during the war he first joined M. Mole & Son where he designed and introduced the Mole vice grip pliers which became a household name. He then worked as managing director of Benton & Stone of Aston Birmingham, best known for the ENOTS range of pneumatic workshop fittings, valves and cylinders now marketed as Norgren. Due to the success of its products Enots outgrew its premises in Aston during the 60s and moved to a greenfield site at Lichfield under Brian's leadership.

During his spare time Brian had a lifelong passion for rebuilding vintage cars to a high standard, having a magnificent workshop at his home in Streetly, and was one of the pioneers in this field. His particular passion was for Bentleys, and he wrote two books with Richard Wheatley to help others with the same interest. The first book 'The Restoration of Vintage and Thoroughbred Cars' was written in 1957 to be followed in 1958 by

'The Maintenance and Driving of Vintage Cars', both books being reprinted several times. Brian maintained a great interest in all things mechanical and was indispensable in the restorations of my Lagonda and Alvis, not only as a source of advice but also in supplying impossible to obtain items.

Brian restored the Lagonda V12 Special Lightweight saloon JPG492, the car which had lapped Brooklands at over 120 MPH average speed before the war, taking from 1966 to 1974 to complete the task.

He was intrigued by model aircraft and attended vintage days at Walsall airport and was much impressed when Barry Hares started his Merlin on a demonstration stand. Also when Gerald Smith ran his Osprey it prompted us to attend his forthcoming lecture at Rolls Royce at Coventry, which we found most interesting and enjoyable.

Brian and his wife Hazel would come to some of the jazz sessions which resulted in him buying an organ to play at home.

It should be noted that Hazel, whose pottery workshop was adjacent to Brian's, also produced masterpieces in ceramics.

Brian's son Paul was constantly accumulating knowledge in this environment as he watched his father restoring vintage cars in his home workshop, and it wasn't long before he built his own radial engine for a model aircraft which was to prove a forerunner of his later great achievements.

PAUL MORGAN

Paul at the wheel of his 1100cc Supercharged Lagonda Rapier

Brian's son Paul was brought up in an engineering tradition. From the age of 15 Paul rebuilt a 1904 DeDion Bouton, a Lagonda Rapier, a Talbot Lago, and a White Steam Car.

Having studied engineering at Aston University, Birmingham he joined Cosworth Engineering where he set up the in-house piston-making department and co-ordinated the development of the Cosworth DFX Indy engine which dominated Indy car racing for almost a decade.

Paul also helped me with some of my aero engine projects, but work on a steam engine for model aircraft came to an abrupt halt when he was flown to Detroit by Learjet. The result of this was that in 1983 he established Ilmor Engineering in Brixworth, Northampton, with partners Mario Illien and Roger Penske, to design and manufacture racing engines for the PPG Cart World series.

Having successfully powered Indy cars to a current total of 116 wins including 7 Indianapolis 500 wins, Ilmor now supplies West McLaren Mercedes with Formula 1 engines and has 19 F1 wins, and powering Mika Hakkinen to two World Championships.

Paul retains his enthusiasm for vintage cars and expertly fitted a high ratio axle in my Lagonda in exchange for my building him a Fairey Swordfish for his home-made radial engine. He is currently assisting in the development of the Maltese Falcon. He enters the London to Brighton veteran car rally each year, and is a great aviation enthusiast and pilot. He maintains a hangar at Sywell which includes a Hawker Sea Fury, a Mustang, a Tiger Moth, a Chipmunk, and a Harvard.

EXPERT HELP!
In a matter of minutes Paul had whipped the cylinders off the Maltese Falcon and decided pistons had to be redesigned with three rings.

Paul explains the intricacies involved in rebuilding the 18 cylinder sleeve-valve radial 54 litre Sea Fury engine.

The Talbot Lago to which Paul has added cycle wings and lights for trips to the pub.

The Merlin in Paul's lounge. Wife Liz has more than horse brasses to contend with when polishing.

A prop-spanner not to be sniffed at for the Mustang engine.

Paul pictured in flight in the Sea Fury.

Footnote: Unfortunately Paul was killed in May 2001 when the Sea Fury overran the runway at Sywell and overturned. His genius will be greatly missed.

LEN VALE-ONSLOW M.B.E.

In 1910 Len's two older brothers Gordon and Harold built a monoplane powered by an inverted Lagonda V-twin engine of 1200 cc capacity. They were the founder members of the Midland Aero Club formed at Castle Bromwich in that year. They flew the machine for 250 yards at a height of 12 feet and one a prize of £250. Later using one wing of the monoplane they made a glider using a bamboo frame fuselage from which Len (aged 9) and being the lightest was suspended. They took it to a hill overlooking the reservoir at Erdington and using a strong 50 yard cord pulled the young pilot at high speed and the glider immediately gained hight and continued in flight until they reached the reservoir when necessarily the cord tension was released. The machine then crashed leaving Len unconscious. They carried him home and laid him on the couch thinking he was dead, and hoping their parents would assume he died of natural causes! He laid in a coma for a fortnight but survived this and many other crashes to achieve many records competing on motor cycles.

One of Len's greatest achievements was to win the Brighton speed trials in 1930 on a 172cc machine of his own design at a speed of 88 M.P.H. It was in 1926 he designed the first all-welded chrome molybdenum frame to be used on a motor cycle. This was incorporated in his own make S.O.S machines (Super Onslow Special).

He was awarded the M.B.E. in 1995 for his services to motor cycling and was featured on television in 'This is Your Life' in 1999. Len is still going strong at the age of 100.

In the 1970s Len paid for and ran a training school for under-privileged and wayward youths including the blind from St Dunstans.

Dennis Howell M.P. assisted by organising a piece of land at Bordesley Green and Len supplied between 6 and 12 motor cycles to encourage them to learn to ride properly (even the partially blind). He also instructed them on good behaviour, to call teachers 'Sir', and refrain from bad language. His efforts reduced the truancy and misbehaviour at Birmingham schools.

Len employed a full time mechanic to service the motor cycles ridden daily at his school. It is interesting and rewarding to note that many of the people who benefited from his inspiration have called in to his shop in later life to thank him for what he did for them.

Michael Aspel presents Len with the famous red book on 'This is Your Life' 1999

S.O.S. MOTOR CYCLES

Len pictured outside his shop in Stratford Road, Birmingham with his original 172cc record breaking bike exactly as used in the 1930 Brighton speed trials. Sir Malcolm Campbell Reported on this event commenting that it was the loudest, fastest bike he had ever seen, and thought that it was rocket propelled as two sheets of blue flame were emitted from Len's expansion chambers. Len commented that 'Running on the alcohol fuel, and having his chin pressed on to the tank, made breathing extremely difficult'. The speed of 88 M.P.H. was unsurpassed by a bike of this small capacity in the 1930s.

Below: Len is guest of honour at Stanford Hall.

Above: Len with a Super Onslow Special road bike. These were produced in both air and water-cooled versions.

KEN KIRBY

Ken was managing director of Kirby (Engineers) Ltd., Pool Street, Walsall, and was not only a brilliant design engineer and inventor but had a great influence on my life. It was Ken who suggested, after my parents were divorced, that I had better get a 'proper' job to enable me to look after my mother, and introduced me to Ken Beardall who was influential in getting me an interview with Columbus Dixon for a speciality salesman's position which was to last 23 years.

This proved a great opportunity and taught me 'positive thinking'- a great asset in my life, together with the ability to get on with a wide variety of people.

Ken designed cardboard box-making machinery and I remember on purchasing a machine from Germany he redesigned it to triple the output. He also patented many machines for cutting irregular shapes. When I designed a floor machine it was Ken who encouraged me and made a prototype in his factory.

An important aspect of inventive engineering is questioning and scrounging and I find it useful to take photos of the projects I require help with or the item itself, to get the interest of the particular expert. He will apply himself to my job with greater enthusiasm and interest than would otherwise be shown.

Ken's greatest asset was a 'Certain Smile' which hopefully I have inherited, which helps to make wheels turn when all else fails.

KEN ARNOLD

Born in Darlaston and educated at Wednesbury Boys High School. He took his first job at Ocker Hill power station in 1953 before doing his two years national service in R.E.M.E. Ken's speciality was coil winding and transformer design , and on leaving the service he went

to work at Woden Transformer Company. Ken then went on to form a partnership in his own company Qualtec Ltd. where he was technical director for twenty years.

I walked into Qualtec and explained that I was going to make miniature magnetos and had no idea of how to design the HT coil. Not only did Ken design several coils for me, and wound many experimental ones, but he also constructed the Minimag magnetising equipment. It is certain that the Minimag Spark Demon HT coil would never have achieved such perfection without his knowledge and input.

In 1990 Ken formed his own company Current Transformer Technology (CTT) off Northgate in Aldridge and continues in his constant search for perfection.

BERTIE BRADNACK

Bertie takes Pardons Hairpin in the SS100 at Prescott Hill Climb 1946.

Bertie, well known sports car enthusiast and racing driver was the M.D. of Walsall Pressings Ltd. where I was to start in the tool room and learn the basis of machining. My first trip with 'Uncle Bertie' was at the age of about 7 when he drove me to Bournemouth in his brand new 3.5 litre SS100, followed by my dad's Wolseley 21 with the families. It was like the hare and the tortoise with Bertie stopping at regular intervals to fall asleep. I woke him when the Wolseley came past.

I was no end impressed and feel today that the SS100 was one of the prettiest sports cars of all time. Bertie, a member of the B.R.D.C. raced at Silverstone and numerous track and hill climb events, also competing in the Monte Carlo Rally on more than one occasion.

A successful entrepreneur, Bertie progressed from building the 'Bradson' carpet cleaner and Walsall Pressings in Cecil Street and moved to a larger premises in Wednesbury Road. Also he was involved with the BRM with the Owen Racing Organisation and Raymond Mays, and interestingly made the Webasto folding roofs – one of which enhances my Austin 7 without noticeable effect on the outside appearance.

On one occasion, in the bar at Silverstone, having narrowly been beaten by Baron de Grafenreid of Germany the Baron said 'Bertie, you went very quickly' On Bertie's response 'Yes but you went like s—t off a shiny shovel' The Baron enquired 'What is this shiny shovel?'

Renowned in Walsall for his flamboyant personality and super sports cars which included a Gull Wing Mercedes 300 SL and a Ferrari Dino. Bertie certainly knew how to drive them in days when motor racing was fun and rivals were good pals.

MIKE HOPE

Mike, brilliant precision engineer from Streetly, together with Graham Madeley formed Brineton Engineering in 1963 working from a small factory in Brineton Street, Walsall. The factory specialised in machining for racing car engines, initially on Bugattis, and gained a world-wide reputation. Later he became involved in Formula 1 engines making parts for Paul Morgan at Ilmor Engineering, Brixworth, and later for other Formula 1 engine companies. His hobby is still Bugattis and he has always been forthcoming with help on my Maltese Falcon engine. Brineton has recently reground the crankshaft to perfection, in their new enlarged modern factory off Green Lane in Walsall. It will be noted that Mike's Bugatti engines perform far better than the originals and much French and Italian can be heard around the factory.

JOHN OWEN

John went to Queen Mary's School in Walsall and later became a qualified engineer working for several midland companies. He is shown holding his twin cylinder Norton engine with his own design 90 degree crankshaft with contra-rotating balance weights. He has calculated that this will completely eliminate vibration from the original 360 degree crank design. John works at the Rover company and brought all the technical departments to a halt to redesign the Minimag camshaft to give high grunt. John also suggested that the conrod caps be made of steel rather than aluminium and directly threaded to eliminate the need for big end nuts. This gives greater clearance for the camshaft in the crankcase.

MINIMAG WORKSHOP

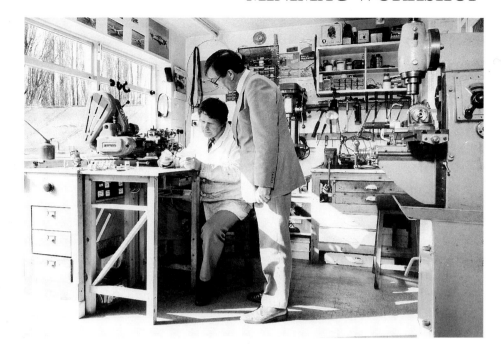

Bobby Pratt (Trumpeter) inspects the Minimag workshop. Myford Lathe on the left, and Centec 2A Vertical and Horizontal Milling machine in the foreground.

Jim screw-cutting on the lathe, using the Norton gearbox.

Pictured below: Side and Front elevation of the Maltese Falcon.

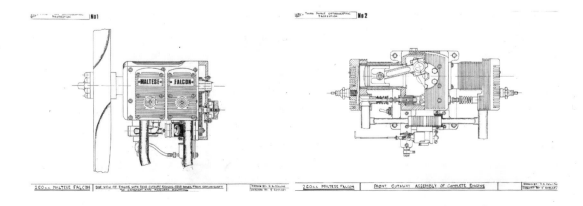

MAGNETOS

It soon became apparent that petrol engines were a great asset in Texaco Competitions, being far more economical than Glo-plug or Diesel motors. The earlier competitions were won with Coil ignition American Sparkies, such as Anderson Spitfire, Forster 99, OK Super 60, Ohlson 60 etc.

Gerald Smith made a magneto for my OS 60 FS which proved to be extremely economical on petrol, eliminating the need for a battery, and later his Skylark powered my Westerner to success. This inspired me to design the Minimag magneto, which was perfected in 1983, after 3 years of concentrated effort.

Left: Minimag Vacuum Potting equipment produces 8 HT Coils on the Turntable. Air is first evacuated completely from the warm chamber, and after the Coils are filled, perfection is obtained by compressing whilst the resin cures.

Right: Magnetising the Alcomax IV Rotor.

Both chamber and magnetiser were designed by Ken Arnold

Left: Miss America, powered by an OS 60 FS, with Crank mounted magneto.

Right: Miss Philadelphia, powered by a Laser 61, with Crank mounted magneto owned by Ron Harris.

MINIMAGS

Crankmounted Magnetos.

Production: Side Laminations are cast into Aluminium bodies using the 'lost-wax' process. Picture shows machined bodies prior to assembly.

Coil Potting: A wound HT coil, on bobbin, with centre laminations in place ready for potting.
Note position of built-in condenser.

Sales: An American customer purchases a magneto kit on the 'field', in the Cotswolds, watched by Bill Linfield (Left).

A **'Gaggle' of Minimags**, at the Texaco Competition. Left to Right; 'Privateer', 'Nimbus', 'Majestic Major' and a KK Falcon', all magnificent performers.

THE MALTESE FALCON
DESIGNED BY JIM SHELLEY

For many years I have flown a 15ft span Taylorcraft using a 100cc Aspera (large Flymo) two stroke engine which turned a 24" diameter by 16" prop at 5000 rpm.

This was sufficient for normal flying in good conditions but inadequate to tow banners in a wind. In common with many large models the high revving two stroke engine and small non-scale prop spoiled the scale effect.

In winter 1997 I decided to make an improved power plant which would drive a scale size prop at similar revs to the full size, i.e. 2000-3000 rpm, that would not only give ample power, but would look and sound right.

Firstly I carved two hardwood laminated props 36" diameter by 24" pitch and found a suitable piston with two rings to base the cylinder design on. The piston was 44mm diameter and I decided to give the engine the same stroke so that it would be very compact using a flat four configuration of the Lycoming 55 hp which powered the original Taylorcraft Plus C monoplane 1939.

The engine was much shorter than the later Cirrus Minor which powered the Auster.

The 'Maltese Falcon' design was influenced by many factors and observations I had made during my experience of flying and watching large models.

I decided to design an engine based on the full size scaled down, rather than continue the trend to scale model engines up.

The Lycoming and Continental flat fours certainly influenced this design, but to make the engine more compact the side valve configuration seemed ideal to turn a large prop at 2000-3000 rpm, reducing total width by some 4" from OHV design – only 12" across heads. This also reduced parasitic drag of overhead valve gear to give maximum low speed torque, and enabling the use of wet sump splash lubrication.

The Achilles heel of pre-war side valve engines was overheating, poor head design, and long stroke causing some vibration.

These problems were addressed as follows:-
1. Cylinders were made in two pieces to give very good airflow through the engine with ample finning.
2. Head design was based on V8 Dragster type reducing volume above piston and valves to absolute minimum, and placing spark plug closer to valves. Compression ratio 6.5 to 1.
3. Square engine 44mm bore, 44mm stroke to reduce vibration.

Low speed torque and reliability being paramount, the 260cc capacity engine started to take on a very compact and business-like appearance. A Minimag magneto is used running at twice engine speed so the one spark per revolution is sufficient to give the distributor two sparks to fire the four cylinders. This also ensures good spark at low revs.

It was decided to retain the very satisfactory 'pull-start' so the 25mm crankshaft was extended at rear. The crank is of the two throw type running on two 25mm ball races and a split bronze centre main bearing. The 10mm camshaft runs on three ball races running directly below the crankshaft. This keeps the engine short and compact, and works as an oil splash into con-rod cups.

The carburettor and float chamber being mounted below the crankcase gives good gravity feed in a steep climb. My tank is in the wing centre section but the low mounted carb will give a good feed from a scuttle tank mounted immediately behind engine.

The rear gear case also serves as a substantial four bolt radial mount through which extends the camshaft driving the distributor.

The 'Maltese Falcon' will provide ample power for models of 100lbs in weight and is ideal for large scale model displays where engine sound and revs will replicate a full size engine.

The Maltese Falcon under test:

Right: Johnny Parsons adjusts the controls on the test stand keeping well clear of the 36" Propeller. A very draughty job.

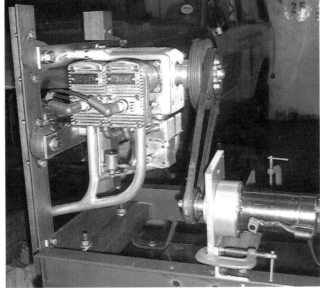

Left: Engine fitted with Flywheel on test bed. Electric free wheeling starter motor, facilitates engine testing. Note the second pulley on the Flywheel which drives a Dynamo so that load can be adjusted on the engine. Picture also shows Float chamber and my infinitely adjustable 'scaled up' model engine carburettor.

Colin Haig, expert polisher at work at R.Thacker & Son, supervised by Peter and David. Colin was responsible for all polishing on vintage cars and Maltese Falcon. "You can't do enough for a good gaffer".

Alan Harper, of the Midland Cutter Grinder Company, continues the family business. Like many one-man engineering businesses he will adapt to any one-off grinding job. He is pictured holding the rotor turbine for John Rock's Jet.

Pictured Right: John Rock, with his home-built Jet engine. The turbine was expertly ground by Alan Harper, above. Accurate engineering of the engine is critical as it exceeds 100,000 revs per min flying a model aircraft at up to 200 M.P.H.

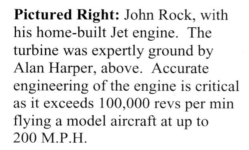

Johnny Parsons, served his apprenticeship as a motor engineer, and for many years ran his own Motor Tuning business, in Walsall. He built and drove Rally cars and shares my interest in model engineering and model aircraft. He has been invaluable, having set up a test-rig with starter motor and generator to provide maximum load for testing maximum B.H.P. Due to his experience in maintaining vintage Bentley's and Bugatti's, his knowledge and input has proved its worth. I think the Bugatti has left him slightly metricated, but in spite of this, his stubborn tenacity together with his knowledge, renders him invaluable. He is a fellow Banjo player so all is forgiven.

The Classic Collection

My first car was an Alvis 12/50 Beetleback followed by a 3 Litre 1924 Red Label Bentley, both were beautiful cars, but unfortunately, I was too young and financially unable to restore them, however, my enthusiasm was ignited.

I bought a Beatt-tuned, 600cc single cylinder racing Norton, for £25.00, from my cousin Terry. After a bump start this went like hell firing every alternate telegraph pole.

I had a 1952 B.S.A Golden Flash Twin, on order and having paid £230.00 and waited some time I finally collected it from Welshpool. To my surprise, although a very nice bike it didn't go like the Norton, and I realised that all things new were not necessarily better. This confounded the well-known expression 'you only get what you pay for'. The penny had dropped.

I selected the vehicles in my collection as being the best in their class and fully proven over the years. I have re-built the Austin 7, Alvis 12/50, Lagonda M45 and the Scott motorcycle featured in this book, to my own specification.

Unlike many 'Dyed in the wool enthusiasts', who restore vintage vehicles, I'm not averse to improvements to increase performance, road worthiness and resistance to corrosion; sometimes using modern seals and even hydraulic brakes on the Austin 7. (Very necessary).

All the featured vehicles are Taxed and have M.O.T certificates and so can be thoroughly relied upon to *'Go Anywhere'*.

LAGONDA
WHAT HAS IT GOT TO DO WITH THE MIDLANDS?

Founded in 1899 in Staines by American Wilbur Gunn the company produced motor cycles followed by tri-cars. The two cylinder air-cooled 45° twin of 1221cc capacity powered the 1904 tri-car and interestingly was used inverted by Len Vale-Onslow's brothers to fly their record breaking monoplane in 1910 at Castle Bromwich. Most Lagondas before the first world war were exported to Russia but in 1924 the 12-24 started to win gold and silver medals in the classic trials. In 1928 the 2 litre racing team did well enough at Le Mans and then the 3 litre won its class at Brooklands in 1929.

Enter the Midlands:

Although the cars were built at Staines the chassis, electrical components and many accessories were of course made in the Midlands.

In the early 1930's, W. O. Bentley had become technical director of Lagonda and, being dissatisfied with the performance of the 3 litre cars, in 1933 fitted the Wolverhampton-built Meadows 4.5 litre engine which definitely made it 'GO'.

In 1935 the Hindmarsh/Fontes Lagonda won the Le Mans. W. O. Bentley had beaten himself and the rest is history. W. O. went on to design the V12 engine which lapped Brooklands in 1939 at an average speed of over 120MPH.

JIM HAS A GO AT SILVERSTONE IN 1976

THE 1933 LAGONDA TOURER 4.5 LITRE
What it lacks in creature comforts it makes up for in its manner of going.

(THE AUTOMOBILE 1934)

Screen flat with aero screens gives an extra 5 M.P.H.

'SILENT JIM', master electrician, responsible for the wiring of all vehicles
in the collection, pulls the wiring harness through, retaining all smoke. (see page on
Electrical Theory).

150 thou was skimmed from head and new
valves fitted giving compression ratio of 9.2
to 1. Aspiration and cooling was improved
by tubular manifold and oil cooler.

ABOVE, JIM works on the wiring.
NB. Original cast manifold shown
later replaced by tubular manifold.
(See right).

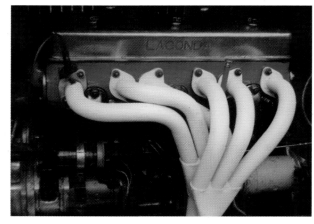

Right: The Lagonda pictured with hood up, which can be removed and stored behind the rear seat.

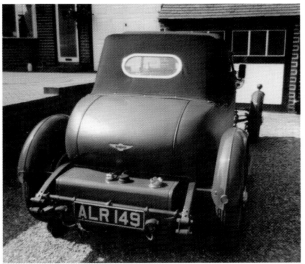

Above: Solid Brass chromed windscreen base gives ample support for Aero screens. On the dashboard can be seen the dual ignition switches for the twelve spark plugs. Six right-side plugs are operated by the magneto whilst the six near-side plugs are coil ignition.

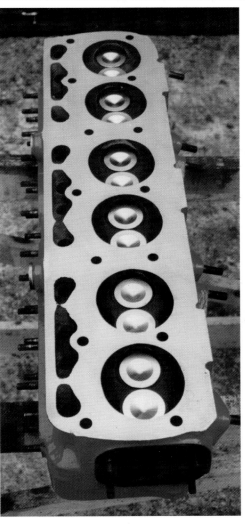

Above: Single door access requires some agility, but is well worth the effort. Passenger seat tilts forward for access to rear seat.

Above: 150 thou has been skimmed from the cylinder head to give a compression ratio of 9.2:1. This improves performance both in top speed and economy and the engine runs just as sweetly using 4 star.

Above: Inside of Bugs Back showing aeromodel planking technique – steamed plywood planks screwed and glued on to an ash and ply frame.

The finished Bugs Back body is very stiff, has no creaks, and is covered in stretch leather which

makes for silent running. This was beautifully done by Ron Passam of Barton under Needwood who was also responsible for the interior leather work. The twenty gallon petrol tank incorporates a 2-way tap which can be turned from inside the boot to give a reserve of fuel.

Left: Brian Ashley of Ashley Competition exhausts is well pleased with the work of his chief 'plumber' Steve Bayley. It will be noted that the tubular manifold is shaped to give good clearance for the distributor feeding into the two down pipes and into the stainless steel silencer and rear pipe.

Lagonda sans Bonnet.
Showing the 4.5 Litre engine made by Henry Meadows of Wolverhampton.
The photo also shows the cast aluminium footplate, twin bronze S.U carburettors and the massive chassis which was guaranteed for the life of the owner.

The Alvis 12-50 surely the most practical and simple design of its era. The OHV pushrod engine not only beat all-comers but is a lesson in simple practicality. The efficient unshrouded brass radiator gives adequate cooling without a fan or water pump. The scuttle tank gives gravity feed so no petrol pump, in fact there is so little to go wrong it is no wonder its reputation for power and reliability was unsurpassed.

Like most brilliant designs the engine looks beautiful and 'Dead right' and is a pleasure to service. It stands up in front of you as it did seventy years ago!

Compare this with what confronts you on opening the bonnet of a modern car.

A near-side view of the 12-50 engine showing the simple and functional design.

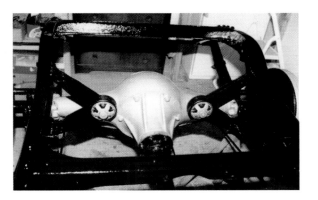

The substantial four speed gear box transmits the power to the heavy duty back axle.

Ducks Back shown with dickie seat open for access.
This rear view confirms the complete lack of consideration shown
by the designers to other road users. This was amplified by the fact
that the Alvis had just passed and was usually in front of you.

The Austin Seven

Herbert Austin introduced the Austin 7 to a sceptical public in 1922. This was to become one of Birmingham's greatest contributions to the motoring public, the first proper large car in 'miniature', as opposed to the crude and unreliable cycle-cars then available.

It was not only a real car, it was made out of first class materials and steels used in larger Austins'.

By 1939, some 290,000 'Sevens' were in service throughout the world, together with 20,000 Big Sevens. The design was licensed to other manufacturers and was produced in France as the Rosengart, in Germany as the Dixi, which became B.M.W's first car and in the U.S.A as the American Austin, later the Bantam. In all its forms, the immortal Seven provided tramfare motoring for motorists and their families the world over, often operating in the most arduous conditions imaginable.

Sports and Racing versions successfully competed against larger and more costly machinery, both on the racetrack and in Off-Road Trials. After years of untiring service many Sevens succumbed to the rigours of the '10 year test' of the early Sixties, but around 6,000 cars have survived worldwide and as a significant sector in today's interest in preserved transport.

This tough little car continues to give an amazing service and enjoyment to yet another generation, whether on simple touring trips, rallies, competition events or pottering about on a summer's day.

'The little friend of all the world'
Literally a car for all reasons.

<u>1932 Austin Seven Box Saloon (Speed Model)</u>

This machine, whilst retaining its original appearance, has been improved by fitting a competition camshaft and SU carburettor giving 60 MPH. This necessitated the following modifications to make it safe for road use:

1. Fitted Minor 1000 hydraulic brakes and master cylinder.
2. Fitted stiffened radius arms.
3. Improved front spring damper
4. Added rear coil springs to stiffen suspension.
5. 12v electrics and halogen bulbs in headlamps.
6. Blinkers in side and tail lights.
7. Webasto sunroof replaces old slide roof.
8. Fibreglass running boards replace corroding type rubber on steel.
9. Aluminium door panels.

THE SCOTT

BUILT TO THE LIMIT GAUGE

THE 600 CC SCOTT FLYING SQUIRREL 1948.

1948 SCOTT 600cc TWO STROKE
WATER COOLED

One of the last *'FLYING SQUIRRELS'* made at Shipley.
This machine has been restored to encompass the best features in the Scott design from 1908 to 1956, and to eliminate some Achilles heels. These include: The Pilgrim oil pump, excessive magneto and primary chain chatter, and clumsy kick-start lever.
The later Birmingham Scotts also got too heavy with noisy dyno, ill-appointed distributor and excessive appendages.
The restoration retains some early Scott concepts i.e. lighter weight, triangulated rigid frame, and suction lubrication, plus some later ones such as Dowty Oleomatic forks, twin front brakes, cush hub and improved lighting. Modern seals and O-rings eliminate leaks, and stainless improves resistance to corrosion.

Left.
Close up photo of the foot change lever and improved folding kick-start.
N.B Alfred Scott invented the kick-start in 1908.

Above.
Close up of my double drip feed into dual crankcase non-return valves. The oil tube in the foreground is to fill measure in petrol tank with Silkolene Pro 2 from oil tank.

Left.
Near side view of engine and radiator showing my improved folding prop-stand.

Right

Off to the Rally. Mounted on the specially constructed trailer which is towed by the Ducksback Alvis, which makes an interesting double exhibit.

MARTIN HONE

Great vintage and classic car enthusiast who not only organised the Birmingham Grand Prix and ran the Opposite Lock Club but more recently organises the annual 'Shakespeare Run' from Coombe Abbey, Coventry, which attracts hundreds of entries world wide.

Martin is renowned for communicating with the Almighty and this run is blessed with the beautiful weather associated with times gone by. This year **BOB WARMAN** (pictured left with Martin) of Carlton TV compered the event. The Jim Shelley Frisco Marching Band and the Eureka Jazz Band provided suitable period music. N.B. When living in Walsall Bob (and his friend Chris Tarrant) were regulars at the Wheatsheaf.

The Lord Mayor of Coventry starts The Shakespeare.
The run is 60 miles with cars being dispatched in chronological order taking in Coventry, Leamington Spa, Solihull, Kenilworth, Henley in Arden, and Warwick
There is a dress theme each year with competitors wearing appropriate attire with a prize for the best outfit.

A view across the field preceding the 'Mass Horn blowing competition' This gives a good idea of the popularity of the event. The Jazz Bands actually marched through the lines of vehicles playing appropriate 20's style numbers.

Both **PAT HARRIS** and my Lagonda cool off and enjoy the atmosphere and sunshine. The Lagonda runs regularly in Martin's vintage car 'Treasure Trails' which take in the most beautiful countryside in Britain – mainly in the Cotswolds. These are organised by Martin's company International Festival Services.

THE TEXACO

VINTAGE DAY AT WALSALL AIRPORT

From left to right: Gerald Smith, Mike Whittard, Fred Barnsley, Mrs M. Smith, Bill Daniel, Mick Smith, Gordon Counsel, Dave Boddington, Vince Redfern, Gordon Williams, and me.

ARTHUR FOX (standing) with his Dolphin.

My Cavalier designed by Ben Shereshaw with its 9ft span and which was powered by a Gordon Williams Mayfly Four Stroke petrol engine.

GERALD SMITH is delighted that ELLIOTT HORWICH won this event since his Falcon was powered by the famous Gerald Smith Skylark.

THE GREAT TEXACO COMPETITION REVIVAL.

In the 1930s the Texaco Cup was awarded for model aircraft duration flying in the U.S.A. and was competed for by free-flight models usually on desert sites followed by cars over many miles.

The British version was started by the Walsall M.A.C. in 1975, later followed by other clubs throughout the U.K. This was a duration competition, but lacking the large open spaces of California rules were modified allowing radio control. They were very simple:

    2cc's of fuel per pound of model weight.

    Rise off ground or deduct 5 seconds for hand launch.

    All models to be designed prior to 1950.

    Weight and authenticity checked with plans by scrutineer.

    Longest flight wins.

My Falcon was powered by a coil-ignition Anderson Spitfire and won many trophies.

Many great aircraft models were designed to compete by Ben Shereshaw, Sal Tabi, Leon Shulmann and others depicted in the Frank Zaic's year books of this era. One of Ben Shereshaw's greatest designs was the Cloud Cruiser. This was kitted by Kiel Kraft in the UK with an enlarged fin and renamed KK Falcon. Wingspan was 8ft and proved excellent in British weather using radio control.

Ben Buckle, of 'Ben Buckle Kits' fame reproduced many of the old designs including the Falcon in the 1980s. He is shown here holding his 'Great Quaker' and is one of the few people who could start an OS80FS Minimag with a flick of the prop! This engine powered his Majestic Major.

TEXACO COMPETITION (Continued)

Left: Jim Herbert starting up his Russell Vulcan.

Right: Members of the Walsall M.A.C on Vintage Day. L to R; Stan Bourke, Fred Barnsley, Gordon Williams, Jim Shelley, Bill Daniel and Eric Redfern.

Left: Fred Barnsley with his magnificent scaled up EROS. Scaling up was allowed under the competition rules, but designs had to be prior to 1950.

Right: My T-Beam on the runway ready for a Class 3 precision flight. Engine is the Gerald Smith Lapwing.

Golden Era Kits

THE POWERHOUSE.

Bill Daniel with son
Robert and myself.

Fred Barnsley, Bill Daniel and Sal Tabi (U.S.A) who
designed the Powerhouse in 1936.

Bill Daniel pictured right holding my Forster 99 Powered Powerhouse.

Bill started Wolverhampton Models & Hobbies over 40 years ago. He and Robert were dedicated enthusiasts of *'Old timers'*, and marketed several kits of the Golden Era.

Robert holding the Golden Era Junior Scram.

Releasing Jim Herbert's 'Meteor Powered Powerhouse'. Jim Herbert designed the Meteor engine.

A young Robert pictured with 'Bunny' Longdon, who made his own design Longdon's Special engines. Bunny's workshop had a dirt floor and his masterpieces were produced on a treadle lathe.

Bill checks the centre of gravity on his Miss Philly, which is powered by one of his home-built engines.

Jim Herbert gets a little help from Dennis Thumpston.

It worked!! Jim Herbert receives his prize from *God* (Gerald Smith).

THE NIMBUS

The Nimbus Airframe.
This shows the planked jig construction of the fuselage, the all-moving tail, the streamlined air wheels and 10 ft wing. This has an Eiffel 400 Wing section, the trailing edge being stiffened and sharpened by a plywood doubler. This give a magnificent glide when combined with the reduced drag of the all-moving stabiliser. The under surfaces are covered in black Polytex, which gives good visibility when flying in competition at high altitude. The aircraft was originally designed by Ben Shereshaw, in 1937, as a free flight Texaco Flyer.

The mighty Nimbus when powered by a Laser 75 Minimag, has proved a formidable competitor in Texaco Competition. Together with my Falcon it has helped fill my Trophy cabinet, shown below.

Pictured Right: The 8 Ft, Kiel Kraft Falcon, which won many competitions powered by a coil ignition Anderson Spitfire, before being superseded by the Nimbus. Interestingly, the design was based on Ben Shereshaw's Cloud Cruiser only the fin shape being altered.

MICK SMITH

The MERCURY IV designed by Mick Smith, was one of the most beautiful cabin model designs. The wing span is 8ft and Mick's original model was flown at Walsall Airport in 1946. My model (shown above) is powered by a 16cc Little Hercules petrol engine.

MICK SMITH, back in England after many years in South Africa, turns up on the Walsall vintage day and as guest of honour presents the prizes.

MABEL'S DREAM

The original Mabel's Dream, that I designed in 1965, a high wing cabin sports model of 65" wingspan.

My dad Jack shows plan view at Sutton Park.

Twice size 11ft span Mabel's Dream powered by an OK Twin 20cc ignition engine.

Inspired by the marvellous designs of Ben Shereshaw, and also Carl Goldberg's sailplane, I redesigned Mabel's Dream as a magnificent soarer. The very lightweight wing has two spar construction with hollow ribs and relies on struts for strength. The wing section is a thinned Clarke Y which gives extremely good penetration to take advantage of any thermal activity which is observed. Unfortunately, since it was designed in1970, it is ineligible for Texaco comps, but glide is astounding.

Above: Terry Shelley shows construction and wing struts.

Below: Rear view

BRITAIN'S FIRST LARGE MODEL AIRCRAFT

The 15 foot span Taylorcraft Auster was built in 1961 by Lou Watson of Market Harborough, an experienced woodworker and boat-builder, first appearing in Aeromodeller in September 1962.

The Auster first flew in 1961 and was built using a mixture of balsa and obechi which was bought at the local woodyard in Market Harborough. The original engine was a 49cc 'Cyclemaster' petrol engine which turned a hand-carved wooden prop. The whole airframe was covered with 14 sq.yds. of nylon and used 1 gallon of dope and weighed in at 37lbs.. The model flew just once while Lou owned it, mainly because it caused such a stir and hostility among the other flying club members at the time, that he sold it on to maintain a quiet life…. shame really.

Bill Daniel wheels out the Taylorcraft in 1969.   Advertising 'Welcome to Walsall'.

Bill was at the counter of his shop 'Models & Hobbies' in Wolverhampton when a customer mentioned there was a massive model aeroplane in a car showroom in Riches Street. When Bill told me the news I immediately rushed round to see if it was for sale. Due to the fact that he could not get any cars in his showroom the proprietor was more than happy to sell it to me. The year was 1968 and its previous five years still remains a mystery. It had a 34cc Jap engine in it which was obviously not suitable to fly it. I rebuilt it as necessary and fitted an 85cc Aspera mower engine. It was flown with dihedral wings using Grundig RC on rudder, elevator and engine only. Response was extremely prolonged and it proved very 'interesting' to fly. Later I fitted a 100cc Aspera and ailerons allowing the dihedral wing to be straightened and fitted with UHF radio. Performance was dramatically improved and the model became familiar at comps. Also used for banner towing and shows on TV.

Recently half flaps were added to shorten take-off and landing runs, pilot and cockpit interior added, repainted silver, with registration GA-MAG replacing Lou Watson's old Co-op number PL-937.

Weight was now 100lbs. So a stronger undercarriage was fitted and in December 1997 I decided to increase the power and so designed the 'Maltese Falcon' 260cc flat four to replicate the Lycoming which powered the 1939 Taylorcraft Plus-C.(Pictured below).

Lou Watson is delighted to see his original plane at the 1999 Cosford Large Model Day. Pictured right is Brian Collins who drew the engineering drawings for the Maltese Falcon.

Aircraft can be easily disassembled and transported in a large estate car.

Bill Daniel and Brian Collins.

Landing at Fradley (100cc Aspera engine).

G. Robinson's impression of the Plus-C powered by the Maltese Falcon.

TAYLORCRAFT PLUS-C FITTED WITH MALTESE FALCON

The Taylorcraft secured to a garden shrub. Should be OK. If we don't rev it too much. N. B A spring balance in the line indicates pull of engine.

Above: Fred Barnsley and Bill Linfield inspect the installation at engine starting party.

Ron Moulton former Aeromodeller editor captures the moment. The Maltese Falcon does not coo like a dove, but is more reminiscent of Bessie Smith on the Black Mountain where all the birds sing bass.

Above: The Maltese Falcon. Front View and on the right installed in the fuselage of the Taylorcraft.

THE MILENBURG
JAZZ BAND

L. to R. John Dickenson (tbn), Gordon Banks (dms) Ray Arnold (bass) Myself, Ray Aston (cnt), Johnny Gauden (pno), and Brian Savegar (cnt).
The Milenburg was the first Jazz Band to form a club in Walsall in the 50's at the Woolpack Hotel in the market.

THE JIM SHELLEY JAZZ BAND playing on a special stage erected in Park Street in Walsall.
L. to R. Norman Field (cnt), Les Roberts (dms), Gordon Whitworth (tpt), Len Rewberry(bass), Ken Freeman (pno), and Stan Lynall (tbn).

Below: In the Lagonda in Park Street with Derek Halford (tmb), and George Barnes (dms) on front seat.

JOHNNY EVERETT (and Murray Smith) taught Jim to play the trumpet and he went on to play in several Midlands bands, among which were Nick Williams Central Jazz Band and Rick Vaughan at the Boat Club in Stourport. Photo shows Johnny Everett and Jim.

Pete Crowson (Clt), Jim Shelley (Cnt), Roger Healey (Bjo), and John Dickenson (Tmb) and, not shown, Stan Moseley (Dms).
This session was at the Pretty Bricks in Walsall and the band also played on Tuesday nights at the Town Hall Hotel in Wolverhampton with additions and variations.

JOHNNY EVERETT joins Jim, giving a two trumpet lead to the Milenburg Band. Also pictured, L. to R. Alan Bailey (Clt), Ray Arnold (Bass), and John Dickenson (Tmb).

GREAT MIDLANDS REED PLAYERS

DAVID LEE

David and I both went to Warwick School at the age of 8 where jazz was frowned upon but played in secret in heavily guarded music rooms. BRIAN LEEKE (piano) and JOHN RICHARDS (tpt) were pupils at Warwick. David played in various bands with me before joining Jimmy Hyde and John Richards in the Second City Jazz Band.

JIMMY HYDE

Jimmy played in the original Midland Jazz Band at the Tamworth Arms and Ex-Captives Club in Hill St. B'ham alongside BOBBY PRATT (tpt) and CHARLIE POWELL (tbn). It was at Hill St. I first met GEORGE HUXLEY from whom I purchased my first G - banjo. Jimmy was a regular member of The Jim Shelley Jazz Band.

NORMAN FIELD

Clarinet and sax virtuoso from Harborne. He played at The Wheatsheaf in the early days with the Ken Ingram and Jim Shelley Bands. His famed Neovox recordings of early jazz are sold worldwide (see discography). His intimate knowledge of early jazz enables him to emulate the styles of many early jazz reedmen such as Don Murray, Frank Teschmaker and Johnny Dodds.

GEORGE HUXLEY

Probably the world's greatest living exponent of Sidney Bechet-style soprano sax playing, and being equally proficient on the clarinet. I first met George at the Ex-Captives Club in Birmingham and purchased from him a John Grey plectrum banjo which is still giving stalwart service 50 years on. George runs his own jazz band and has only recently retired from his company specialising in fuel injection.

Bob Smith

THE EAGLE JAZZ BAND

Ken Ingram's Eagle Jazz Band was formed in 1951 and achieved great popularity. The band has played on radio, television, and had engagements in every major town and city in the Midlands.

During the concert at Birmingham Town Hall (above) Mary Orr shared equal popularity with Ottilee Patterson who was singing with the Chris Barber Band.

Personnel (l.-r.) Bob Smith (Cln), Roy Sanders (Dms), Ken Ingram (Tpt), Myself(Bjo), Gordon Bradford (Tba), Tony Hobson (Tmb), and Mary Orr (Vocals).

Some of the regular venues played by the Eagle were the Golden Cross at Aston, the Queens at Reservoir Road Erdington, the Golden Eagle in Hill Street Birmingham, and regular Saturday and Sunday evening sessions at the Old Crown in Deritend, and, of course, a weekly session at The Wheatsheaf in Walsall. At these sessions a Laurel & Hardy film was put on during the interval by Bob Smith who also made a Frankenstein type film featuring members of the band which was shown during the interval.

THE OLD CROWN, DERITEND

The Old Crown, built in 1368, was Birmingham's oldest building and a hot bed of jazz. It may be of interest that Jim's interview for a job as a salesman with Columbus Dixon took place in the office which was to the right of the centre arch. (Jim got the job which lasted for 23 years).

Ken Ingram's Eagle Jazz Band was formed in 1951 and achieved great popularity having played on both Radio and Television. The Old Crown shown above, was the home of the regular weekly Jazz Club. Interval entertainment was organised by Bob Smith, Clarinettist, with a regular Laurel & Hardy Film Show.
The Band was so popular the weekly show was increased to twice weekly. Both Saturday and Sunday sessions played to full houses.

THE GAUMONT, WALSALL

Back row L. to R. Johnny Gauden (pno), Roy Saunders(dms), Ken Ingram(tpt), Cinema Manager, Gordon Bradford(tba). Seated: Tony Hobson(tbn), Bob Smith(clnt), and myself(bjo).Photo, taken outside the Gaumont Cinema, The Bridge, Walsall.

It is interesting to note that many musicians began their careers playing for Ken Ingram and still learn from his encouragement.

Bobby Pratt took over from Ken Ingram on trumpet and the tuba of Gordon Bradford was replaced by Nick Williams on string bass. Barry Norman replaced Roy Sanders on drums.

The Eagle Jazz Band, with some personnel changes, is still playing today. They produced a video entitled 'The First 45 years of the Eagle Jazz Band' which in addition to the music has some hilarious content. I still sit in on banjo when requested.

BY ROYAL APPOINTMENT

In addition to getting free drinks it was quite normal for the band to be offered food in the interval.
L. to R. Bobby Pratt (Tpt), Bob Smith (Clt), Jim (Bjo), Tony Hobson (Tbn), Barry Norman (Dms),
Nick Williams (Bass).

1974 was a significant year for the Eagle Jazz Band. They were booked to perform for the Bentley Drivers Club at the Dorchester Hotel (guest of Honour W.O.Bentley). The dance band (Confrey Phillips Society Orchestra were impressed to the extent of booking the Eagle to play at a private function for the Queen and Royal Family at Goodwood House two weeks later. Incidentally Tony Shelley was performing this same night at The Magic Circle banquet at the Café Royal in Regent Street with David Nixon. Both functions were attended by parents Jack and Marjorie Shelley.

Later that year the band appeared on Hughie Green's Opportunity Knocks when, unfortunately Jim's rendition of 'Those Magnificent Men in Their Flying Machines' came up against Lena Zavaroni's acclaimed performance knocking it into second place.

In October Jim was invited to play with Graham Stewart's band at the Gashouse in Greenwich Village, New York. He also sat in with Roy Eldridge and Joe Jones at Jimmy Ryans.

On returning to England he formed the Jim Shelley Jazz Band, but still occasionally performs with the Eagle. The Jim Shelley Band in various forms played through until 1985 when the Frisco Band was formed.

THE TROUSERS

To the untrained eye it may seem strange to observe a fellow, apparently down on his luck, stalking along like a leopard in a pair of brown trousers with black spots. It may appear even stranger that the location is Walsall bus station, an area not normally known as 'Leopard country', but there is a perfectly logical explanation.

I was on tour with the 'Cutty Sark Dixieland Band' but on arrival at Frankfurt airport, to my dismay, I discovered I had left my black band trousers at home. Since the first engagement was at the Royal Spa Hotel in Baden Baden a quick tour was made of all the clothes shops in town with dismal results. All the trousers were for seven foot tall men and made of thick flannel and obviously intended for overwintering on a mountain top without the benefit of a log cabin. Desperation overcame the need for flies and buttons but the ladies outfitters proved to be equally uninspired and nothing fitted.

It was now 4.30pm and getting dark so urgent action was called for. I bought a one litre aerosol of black cellulose from a car accessory shop, and shaking it vigorously rushed back to the hotel. The coach was waiting so the band went to the Royal Spa for a sound check and meal. Borrowing bass player Don Gray's trousers I was left to spray my own brown trousers. Selecting a bush which was well illuminated from a shop window, spraying commenced. Half way through, as I was turning the trousers to do the back, the incredulous shop keeper appeared in the doorway and made some observations and guttural remarks in German. My explanation that I was 'English' appeared to satisfy him and spraying continued. Finish spraying of finer details like pockets and flies was done in the bedroom until the whole litre can was used up.

By this time the coach reappeared to collect me and, having had a quick shower, I leaped into the uniform and rushed down the stairs from the fume filled bedroom and jumped on to the coach. I positioned myself between the empty coach seats to allow the air to circulate around the trousers.

On entering the ballroom a spontaneous round of applause came from the band as the trousers looked very good and even retained their creases. Whilst the band had a meal I decided to go for a walk to get some air round the trousers as the fumes were still intense. On entering a bar and ordering a beer the girl on the next stool, having recovered from a bout of coughing, opened her handbag to check the cap on her nail polish. My lack of German ensured the mystery remained unresolved.

Once the fumes had subsided the trousers were a great success and the tour played Dusseldorf without further incident.

On returning home I took the trousers to Harris Cleaners in Walsall and was told they would be ready next day. Suspecting they may have difficulties I left a week before returning to collect the aforementioned leopard-like apparel. Harris were most apologetic, saying that it had never happened before, and gave me three free cleaning vouchers and on my suggestion gave the trousers to Oxfam.

JIM SHELLEY.

THE WHEATSHEAF

The Wheatsheaf Hotel in Birmingham Street, Walsall was a renowned Goodtime Jazz venue in the 50s, 60s, and 70s. The proprietors were Norman and Jean Bent, whose daughter Leila Williams became Miss Great Britain and went on to become a TV presenter. During the early days Marjorie Shelley (Jim's mother) served behind the bar, and various well known entertainers performed there. Amongst those were several Midlands pianists including Reg Keirle, Johnny Gauden , Bill Bickerton, Len Newbury, Duncan Swift, and Tommy Burton. Also the Freddie Degville Trio (including Paul Degville) performed Django Reinhart's 'Hot Club de Paris' String Quartet music. Later Marjorie took over the tenancy and the music continued unabated – jazz bands upstairs and piano/vocals downstairs. In these days it was almost impossible to get a seat, and should nature dictate customers were passed overhead and out through the window, sometimes being caught up in the fan. Vocalists included Little Ricky, Ron Bough, Angel Brown, and George Melly. Among the visitors at this time were Bob Warman, Chris Tarrant, and Derek Hobson who all lived locally. Among the jazz bands playing upstairs were the Eagle, George Huxley, and the Jim Shelley Jazz Band.

MARJORIE SHELLEY (Tenant of The Wheatsheaf) with her beloved Mercedes 280SL.

Opening of the newly refurbished Bar

L. to R. Dougie Naylor, Marjorie, Cllor Wright and Carol. Egress through the transom of the front bay window, having proved to be advantageous in emergencies, was retained.

Due to heavy use the turnover in pianos was considerable. The band ones being dropped into the street through the upstairs window when they reached the end of their useful life. Carrying the new ones up was considerably more difficult and time consuming.

THUNDERFOOT BURTON'S CELESTIAL THREE

Tom was joined by Wakka Wakefield (drums) who later formed the Fylde Coast Jazz Band and Jim for regular evening and Sunday lunchtime sessions in the Wheatsheaf bar to a packed house. In the words of P.G.Wodehouse 'It is inadvisable to face a hostile audience with orange juice sloshing round inside you'. The Celestial Three descended on London entering the ongoing skiffle contest at the Metropole Theatre in Edgware Road. Since they did not know any skiffle their renditions of Steam Boat Bill and Robert E. Lee, with Tom playing guitar, were sufficient to win the heat. Skint at the time they ate sugar from coffee bars and were playing in a basement when joined by a guest trumpet player who turned out to be Nat Gonella (the British Louis Armstrong). He remained a lifelong friend of Tom. Funds were so tight that we pooled our money and bought four gallons of petrol and one gallon of paraffin for the return journey to the midlands. Needless to say we could not afford to go down for the next heat at the Metropole.

Tom later played regular sessions on BBC TV on Pebblemill at One, and went on to become one of the great performers on the British jazz scene. Tom's versatility showed when he recorded Lavender Blue which topped the Jamaican hit parade. His accent was so good they were amazed to find him to be 'a White Cockroach'. When he sang and played Fats Waller he not only sounded like him but looked like him.

George Melly rated him as the finest exponent of Fats Waller's playing in this country.

Thos. William Burton (1935-2000)

Legendary Black Country jazz pianist, singer and bandleader.
'When God made Tommy Burton he must have sat about for weeks wondering if he'd gone too far. Certainly he never repeated the exercise, and Tommy stands unique'. So wrote the late Gerry Anderson.

Tom and I were lifelong friends but Tom suffered a stroke in May 1999 and his speech was impaired. A fighter to the end, Tom continued to play piano and joined my Frisco Band for his last big concert on July 22nd 2000 at Saltram House, Plymouth, which was attended by 2000 people. Everybody stopped dancing when Tom played 'Stumbling' (by Zess Confrey). The tumultuous applause produced an encore of fine boogy-woogy piano playing and a standing ovation.

He was looking forward to further concerts with the Frisco but unfortunately after attending the Bude Jazz Festival he died on September 2nd 2000.

Tommy's final performance with the 'Frisco Band at Saltram House Plymouth July 22nd, 2000

Beneath the wild image Tommy was a sensitive man and through his charitable work was able to provide over twenty guide dogs for the blind.

What he excelled in was giving everyone in the audience a great night out which they would not forget in a hurry. The jazz scene will not forget Tommy Burton in a hurry either.

Tom's funeral was attended by 800 fellow musicians and friends from all over Britain and abroad. Pictured below is the 14 piece Frisco Eureka Parade Band at the graveside. The band preceded the hearse playing 'Just a closer walk with Thee', 'Oh didn't he ramble', and after the service, at Dot's request, 'Walking with the King' which summed up the thoughts of the musicians both playing and listening.

L. to R: Tony Hobson, Terry McGrath, Mike Owen, Jim Wood, Wakka Wakefield, Phil Matthews, Mike Haslum, George Huxley, Jim Shelley, Pete Cotterell, Gordon Whitworth, Johnny Everett, Dennis Armstrong, and Chris Mercer.

WHEATSHEAF REGULARS

Johnny Gauden: Child prodigy and gifted pianist in demand with many Bands. Played regular solo piano in the Bar.

Eddie Mathews: Ex-B'ham University Lecturer and all-round good egg. Pictured playing with the Eagle Jazz Band, in the upstairs Jazz room.

Len Rewberry: Regular Base player with the Jim Shelley Jazz Band. Len originally played in the Dance Bands at Walsall Town Hall and toured with my Milenburg Jazz Band.

Brian Bates: A very sensitive and versatile musician from Coventry, became a regular with the Jim Shelley Jazz Band. He now plays with the Terra Buena Band and the Johnny Parsons Tame River Jazz Band.

Among the regular pianists at the Wheatsheaf was Len Newbury, pictured seated at the piano, with John Sparky. Len was a prolific composer and walking encyclopaedia of lyrics. Before the war he accompanied Gracie Fields and was an inspiration to many Midlands pianists including Tommy Burton and Reg Keirle. Among his compositions was 'Hold on to your Dreams' and the title song for 'When it's Summer in Summer Lane' which had a short run in the West End. The brevity of this run was probably due to Londoners not realising that Summer Lane (in Birmingham) was heavily industrialised with the Crocodile Works on one side and the Salutation pub on the corner. The opening lyric 'You can see the palm trees swaying' fell on stony ground. His last famous composition was Winnie's Waltzing Rag which he wrote for Winifred Atwell. Len used to walk 10 miles to play at the Wheatsheaf in Walsall from his home in Edgbaston, often walking home via the cricket match at West Bromwich (probably a round trip of well over twenty miles).

LEN NEWBURY

REG KEIRLE

Well-known Black Country pianist, raconteur and artist, not only entertained at the Wheatsheaf often alternating with Tommy Burton but was also responsible for many murals at the Wheatsheaf and famously described me as the Jack Buchanan of Pleck.

BILL BICKERTON

as drawn by Reg Keirle often played piano with the Jim Shelley Jazz Band and was another regular at the Wheatsheaf.

Above: Kenny Freeman at the Wheatsheaf piano.

Left: Jimmy Hyde (Cln) and Brian Bates (Tpt) lead a jiving session with Doreen and June.

Stan Lynall (Tmb), Brian Bates (Tpt), and Jimmy Hyde (Cln) front the Jim Shelley Jazz Band.

Dave Margoroni (Bass) and Bill Bickerton (Piano).

Barry Phillips joins the band on trombone.

Band moves to the Crest Hotel. Brian Casson (Tbn), Jim Wood (Helicon), Brian Bates (Tpt), Mike Haslum (Dms), JS, and Jimmy Hyde (Sop. Sax).

SOME WELL-KNOWN MIDLAND MUSICIANS

THE CUTTY SARK DIXIELAND BAND played regular sessions at the Albion at Stafford. Pictured left: Alan Pendlebury (Tbn), me, Gordon Whitworth (Tpt), Len Rewberry(Bass), & Cutty Sark (Clnt). Pictured right: Cutty Sark(clt), Me and Pat (birthday girl), Tony Hobson(tmb), and Pat Hobson, listening intently, at the County Hotel, Walsall.

Above left: Bob Smith (clt), ex leader of the Eagle Jazz band alongside Gordon Whitworth(tpt) joins the Frisco on tour. Above right: Derek Halford sings Sugar with Cutty on clarinet playing with the Cutty Sark Dixieland Band.

Pictured left: Ken Littler, pianist with the Frisco, playing at the '100 Club' Oxford Street, London.
Pictured right: The Frisco playing at the Calvert Trust, Keswick in May 2001.

EMPEROR
NORTON'S
HUNCH

EMPEROR OF THE UNITED STATES AND
PROTECTOR OF MEXICO

NORTON
Joshua

Joshua Norton reigned as Emperor of the United States and Protector of Mexico for over 20 years until his death in 1880. Born in London in 1819, he built up a considerable fortune in South Africa and San Francisco dealing in foodstuffs and property. In 1853 Norton saw his chance to hit it really big by cornering the rice market. He bought and held all available rice; as prices soared he foresaw enormous profits. His castles in Spain crumbled, however, when several ships laden with rice sailed into San Francisco bay. The market was glutted, prices dropped and Norton lost everything. In 1856 he filed for bankruptcy.

Within a year he had confided in several friends that he was actually Norton 1, Emperor of California. However in 1859 he decided that the State of California did not have the authority to name him Emperor and that, in order for his title to be legitimate, he would have to be Emperor of all the United States. Accordingly, he handed over the following proclamation to the editor of the San Francisco Bulletin, who printed it without comment.

At the pre-emptory request and desire of a large majority of the citizens of the United States, I, Joshua A. Norton, declare and proclaim myself Emperor of the U.S. and in virtue of the authority thereby in me vested, do hereby order and direct the representatives of the different states of the Union to assemble in Music Hall, of this city, on the last day of February next, then and there to make such alteration in the existing laws of the Union as may ameliorate the evils under which the country is labouring, and thereby cause confidence to exist, both at home and abroad, in our stability and integrity.

Norton 1 Emperor of the United States.
17th September 1859.

He felt that the United States needed a strong head of state, reluctantly he dissolved the Republic, abolished Congress and the office of President and announced that he would henceforth rule personally. When this, like so many other of his Imperial decrees, was disregarded Norton was not shaken. At the outbreak of civil war he summoned both Lincoln and the rebel leader, Jefferson Davis, to his presence and issued a decree ordering hostilities to cease.

The citizens of San Francisco accepted his decrees with great good humour and respect even acknowledging their responsibility to contribute to his upkeep. The Imperial Palace was a small room in a seedy lodging house, but the 50 cent-a-night charge was paid by loyal subjects. Norton's wardrobe was a mixed bag of army and navy uniforms, outlandish hats and elaborate walking sticks. When it began to grow shabby he issued a decree: *'Know ye that we, Norton the First, have divers complaints from our liege subjects that our Imperial wardrobe is a national disgrace'*
The following day the city council met and voted funds for a new uniform, to be supplied by the prestigious firm of Bullock & Jones, Tailors by appointment to His Imperial Majesty.

Norton's scrip (homemade 25 and 50 cent notes) was accepted freely by restaurateurs and shop keepers; he had free passes to theatres and upon his entrance the audience always rose to their feet.

Like many public figures , Norton was subject to interference in his life by complete strangers. False telegrams were a favourite ploy and one wag attempted to arrange a marriage for Norton with the widowed Queen Victoria. Telegrams of congratulations on the proposed match purported to come from Tsar Alexander, Disraeli, and Ullyses S. Grant.

Robert Louis Stevenson admired the people of San Francisco for fostering and encouraging this 'harmless madman'. They did so because Norton brought colour to their city and because, as a judge remarked, rebuking a policeman who had arrested Norton for lunacy, he had '*shed no blood, robbed no one and despoiled no country, which is more than can be said for most fellows in the king line*'.

He also promoted some hair-brained schemes including a plan to build a bridge from San Francisco to Oakland. During the 1860s and 70s he was San Francisco's most notable character. He died in 1880 and 30,000 people filed past his grave.

LU WATTERS, band leader and composer, was largely responsible for the revival of, and enthusiasm for, post-war jazz. This started at the Dawn Club in San Francisco in 1946, featuring the two trumpet powered front line, the inspiration for the Shelley band. His most famous composition being Emperor Norton's Hunch

His name was immortalised when the Golden Gate bridge was built and perpetuated by Lu Watters composition 'Emperor Norton's Hunch'.

It was the Yellow Melodisc recordings of Lu Watters that penetrated as far as England and were an inspiration to many up and coming British bands.

It was at a concert at Birmingham Town Hall that Jim heard Graham Bell's Australian Jazz Band and realised that Watters music had penetrated the antipodes. The sound was inspirational but lay dormant for many years before Jim formed the eight piece Frisco Jazz Band in 1985 with like-minded enthusiastic jazz musicians. It was an immediate success and has been in demand at jazz clubs and festivals ever since.

JIM SHELLEY'S FRISCO JAZZBAND

The eight piece Frisco Band recreates the music recorded by the Lu Watters Yerba Buena Jazz Band on America's West Coast before and after the second world war. This bouncy good time jazz can be heard at many U.K. jazz festivals throughout the year and is the ideal music for the listening and dancing jazz aficionado.

Watters' records – the yellow and magenta Melodisc 78 rpm labels of beloved memory to those old enough - which became available here in the late 1940s were instrumental in the revival of interest in classic period jazz and many musicians starting then developed an enthusiasm for the Watters' style of music.

Watters was fascinated by 1920's jazz particularly the music of King Oliver, the Armstrong Hot 5s and 7s, and Morton's Hot Peppers. His bands reflected that passion, as does the music of the Jim Shelley Frisco Jazzband. The music he produced thus inspired came out with a bright free-wheeling good time sound – albeit white - which radiates an unmistakable and immediately recognisable vitality.

The Shelley Band, with its emphasis on well-structured ensemble playing, follows the same path that Watters trod earlier and is almost wholly inspired by an enthusiam for the giants of the 20s classic period.

Tuesday 25th February 1986 saw the first outing of the band (after a whole 1¾ hours rehearsing!) at the Boundary Hotel, Walsall. The band had an unchanged personnel for the last 13 years until October 1999 when Dennis Armstrong replaced Gordon Whitworth on lead cornet.

JIM SHELLEY – banjo, titular head and self-employed miniature engine and magneto manufacturer. Along with Jim Wood, the Frisco Jazzband was Jim's brainchild. Jim's rock-steady banjo is one of the cornerstones of the Frisco's powerful rhythm section. His vocal contributions include the band's signature tune – San Francisco.

DENNIS ARMSTRONG – lead cornet, Yorkshireman. By the age of 17 Dennis was playing in pubs in the Bradford and Leeds area and played in many bands before forming the Excelsior Jazz Band. He went on to lead the Yorkshire Post Jazz Band and Great Northern Jazz Band. He left Yorkshire for Bristol in 1996 before joining the Frisco band on first cornet in October 1999.

"WATTY" WATHEN – clarinet. Watty's great resemblance to Bessy Smith only goes as far as his singing, but his fierce Doddsian clarinet style is essential to bite through the powerful brass ensembles. A university man.

CHRIS MERCER – second cornet, Yorkshireman, started playing in the late 40s in a band trying to emulate the Yerba Buena. A publicity consultant, he has been specialising on second cornet for the last 20 years.

TONY HOBSON – trombone, another full-time musician whose style is a perfect combination between Kid Ory, Turk Murphy, and Honore Dutrey. His shouting tailgate trombone is an excellent foil to the strong dual cornet lead.

KEN LITTLER – piano, a very accomplished full-time musician who can play in a great variety of styles. His ragtime style is ideal for ensemble and solo work alike.

JOHN PENN – another brilliant pianist has now replaced Ken apart from local gigs.

JIM WOOD – Yerba Buena tuba, Retired university man, Jim's solid, accurate bottom line is an essential for the band's powerful ensemble work and his introduction chorus to several blues numbers are a highlight.

MIKE HASLUM – drums, the baby of the band! A retired civil servant. His early playing days were with Dan Pawson. Mike is a great devotee of the classic rhythm men and in particular Baby Dodds.

The band has regularly been a main feature at the biggest festivals in the U.K. and topped the bill at Gelsenkirchen (Germany) Jazz Day in September 1992.

Back row: Jim Wood, Chris Mercer, and Dennis Armstrong.
Front row: Watty Wathen, Mike Haslum, Me, John Penn, and
Tony Hobson.

Pictured right: Jim Wood on the Yerba Buena Tuba.

UP AGAINST IT!

Should any band member ask Jim Wood the directions
for Summer Lane or Aston Brook Street his response
is usually something less than courteous, and sometimes includes an expletive which may appear a rather
strong response for an apparently innocent question.
For three months Jim's Yerba Buena tuba lacked a
certain clarity in both attack and volume. This is why
he decided to clean the bores with a drain-cleaning
spring rod. It was this operation which produced an
A-Z Guide which some nut had pushed down it.
Happily thereafter all was restored to normal.

Pictured left: Gordon Whitworth, lead trumpet.
Gordon played with the Jim Shelley Jazzband before
joining the Frisco, with whom he played for 15 years.
He contributed greatly to its popularity adding vocals
and variety to its repertoire and recordings.
Gordon left the band in October 1999 to be replaced
by Dennis Armstrong on lead cornet.
I would like to thank Gordon for his significant
contribution and accurate melody lead in the Frisco
Jazzband.

THE SHELLEY FAMILY

Edward Shelley

Portrait painted by George Willott, ex Principle of Walsall School of Arts & Crafts.

Edward Shelley, my Grandfather, who was the Mayor of Walsall and Founder of the Edward Shelley School, which had a high reputation for education. It is now part of the Walsall Art College and continues as the Shelley Campus. He also Founded Shelley's Chemists in Palfrey, in 1894, and Jack, my Father, followed in his footsteps opening a shop in Caldmore Green. This was later extended to a total of 8 Shops, with the stores in Forum Passage. I used to work at the Stores and deliver the goods.

Jack and Marjorie Shelley, my Mother and Father, had a house in Charlemont Road, Walsall at the time I was born. I now live within half a mile of that house. I have not wandered too far.

THE SHELLEY FAMILY

Hillcrest, Highgate Road, Walsall.

Jack Shelley with Brandy.

Hillcrest, the family home, was the scene of much diverse activity. During the war Micky Rooney and Bobby Breen were billeted there from Fradley R.A.F. Among the visitors were Diana Dors, Arthur Lucan, Derek Roy, Reg Dixon, Patrick Allen, Richard Wattis, James Hayter, Phyllis Calvert, Sylvia Simms, and B.B.C. band leader Billy Ternent. The lounge proved a good recording studio for myself, Tommy Burton and Stan Lynall. Fred Barnsley said his recording of the George Huxley Band was the best he had done, due to the excellent acoustics.

My father Jack was not an immediate convert to jazz, and during late night rehearsals the phone would ring from his bedroom asking how much longer had he got to put up with this din. It was some time before he was converted from Charlie Kunz and James Last to sitting on the front row of many of my Band's concerts. His favourite request was Snake Rag. As captain of Walsall Golf Club Jack booked the Jim Shelley band to perform there where the audience was rather more refined than usual and the modified lyrics of 'A Hard Man is Good to Find' were received with a wave of apathy.

The family pharmacy business started by my grandfather Edward Shelley in 1894 was continued by Jack, and later Tony, whilst I opted out of this profession and became apprenticed at Bertie Bradnack's Company, Walsall Pressings, which was the start of my engineering interest.

Magician, Brother Tony, poses in front of the Hyatt Hotel on the Lagonda. Brother Larry, a landscape gardener, poses with my Lion, and Marjorie and me in the garden of her home.

TERENCE BURTON SHELLEY

Cousin Terry races his 500 cc Gold Star B.S.A in the Senior Clubman's TT on the Isle of Man in 1952. In was in 1952 that terry sold me his 1930 Beat-tuned 600 cc Norton. This was a racing bike (for the side-car class) which was converted back to solo and required a "run and bump start". The long stroke single cylinder engine gave very high performance, firing every alternate telegraph pole.

Terry was also a virtuoso on both piano and organ.

He is pictured right, at the console of the mighty Wurlitzer at the West End Cinema in Birmingham, in 1952. He used to rise through the floor, often in white evening dress, playing his signature tune "Twilight Time". His performances were received with tumultuous applause and his version of the "Teddy Bears Picnic" was the envy of many other organists, who used to come to the cinema just to listen to Terry.

Left: Terry pictured with his 1924 Model 'T' Ford Roadster. He restored this car to concours condition in his immaculate workshop. Like me Terry was a 'Blacksheep' of the pharmaceutical who later joined Columbus Dixon and took great interest in engineering from the size of steam-rollers downward.

TONY SHELLEY

My younger brother Tony followed about 4 years behind me through Warwick School and later King's School, Sherborne. In his early years his ambition was to be a magician but, probably sensibly, he saw the insecurity of a life in show-business and opted for the security of a steady job and took up the family tradition of pharmacy. For many years he ran his own shop in Birmingham before taking over the family shop from my father in Walsall. However the magic bug had bitten and many times could he be caught practicing his sleight of hand in preference to learning the interactions of digitalis and phenobarbitone. At the age of 17 he joined the local Wolverhampton Circle of Magicians and such was his enthusiasm that six years later he had progressed to become their youngest-ever president. From this position he joined the British Magical Society (the world's oldest magical society) of which he has now served two terms of presidency and has been made a fellow. In 1969 he won the British Ring Shield (the equivalent of the national championships). Ten years later he became national President of the British Ring of the International Brotherhood of Magicians. It was from this position that he was recognised internationally and eight years later became International President of the I.B.M., one of the highest positions in the world of magic, and only the third Englishman to attain this honour. His crowning glory during his year of office was during a visit to Moscow where he inaugurated the organisation's first Ring behind the Iron Curtain. Twenty five years ago he was called to membership of the prestigious Inner Magic Circle, with Gold Star for performing ability. His magic has taken him around the world with performances in the

U.S.A., the U.S.S.R., Italy, France, Germany, Belgium, Australia and New Zealand. At home he has performed in most major theatres in England, including the famous London Palladium, and London venues such as The Dorchester Hotel, Grosvenor House and the Café Royal. Besides completing many tours with the Ken Dodd Laughter Show he has made numerous cameo TV appearances as well as performing his award winning act on the David Nixon TV Magic Show. In recognition of his International Presidency Tony had conferred upon him the title of Honorable Colonel of the State of Kentucky so we guess that he is the first, and probably the only, Colonel we have had in the Shelley family.

JIM'S OBSERVATIONS

A.   LIFE IS NOT FAIR AND DON'T EXPECT IT TO BE SO.

(A master at Warwick School having laid the ruler on an innocent youth)

B.   RULES ARE FOR THE GUIDANCE OF WISE MEN AND THE OBEDIENCE OF FOOLS.

(Douglas Bader)

C.   ONE HAS TO KNOW WHEN TO BE, AND WHEN NOT TO BE, AMONG THOSE PRESENT.

(P.G.Wodehouse)

D.   HE WHO NEVER MADE A MISTAKE NEVER MADE ANYTHING.

(Anon.)

E.   MOST GOOD ADVICE COMES LATE.

(Anon)

F.   NOBODY LOVES A SMART ARSE.

(Anon)

G.   BEWARE OF OVER SIMPLIFICATION: "ANY FOOL CAN SEE THAT IT'S FLAT"

(Final words of the President of the Flat Earth Society)

H.   THE DIFFERENCE BETWEEN GENIUS AND STUPIDITY IS THAT GENIUS HAS LIMITS.

(Einstein)

I.   HASTE IS THE ENEMY OF PERFECTION.

(Beau Brummel)

THE JIM SHELLEY FACT FILE.

General & Work	Music	Aero Modelling & Engineering	Vintage Restorations
Born 1933 Walsall			
1941 Warwick School	First Piano lessons		
1943		Built a Hornet and Frog 45	
1947		Bought a Mills Diesel 1.3 cc.	
1948 King's School Sherbourne	Syncopation lessons from Frank Drew in Palfry.	Joined Walsall Model Aero Club.	350 cc. Ex-WD Triumph Motor Cycle.
1950 Bookkeeping Clerk.	Self taught Banjo.		1931 Norton 600 cc Motorcycle.
1951 Walsall Pressings.			1930 Alvis 12/50 Beetleback.
1952 Shelley's Chemists – Assistant and Driver		Toolmaker's Apprentice.	B.S.A Golden Flash 650 cc. Motor Cycle.
1953			1924 Bentley Red Label.
1954 Rubery Owen – Lorry Driving.		Designed Mabel's Dream. 65" Cabin Mono Plane.	
1957 Joined Columbus Dixon.			
1962	Joined Ken Ingram's Eagle Jazz Band. Started the Milenburg Jazz Band Toured Scotland. Played with the Tommy Burton at the Wheatsheaf.		1948 Scott Flying Squirrel Motor Cycle.
1968		Bought 15 Foot Taylorcraft, rebuilt it and flew it.	Bought 1933 Lagonda, commenced rebuild.
1974	Eagle Jazz Band played for Royal Family and W.O.Bentley. I played in New York, and formed the Jim Shelley Jazz Band on my return.	Designed 11 Foot span Mabel's Dream.	Raced Lagonda at Silverstone and Oulton Park.
1977		Met Gerald Smith, who made my first Magneto. Won first Texaco Competition, with Skylark powered Westerner	Bought 1932 Austin 7 Box and rebuilt it.

General and Work (Continued)	Music (Continued)	Aero Modelling & Engineering (Cont)	Vintage Restorations (Continued)
1980 Left Columbus Dixon			
1983 Formed Minimag Company			
1985	Formed the 'Frisco Jazz Band.	Made first Minimag. Built Nimbus.	Bought and rebuilt Alvis 12/50 Ducksback.
1992		Minimags win 50 Competitions.	
1993			Entered Alvis in Gordon Bennett Rally in Southern Ireland
1997	Dutch Discography includes over 100 recordings.	Built first Yacht, The Emperor Norton.	Rebuilt Scott Squirrel Motor Cycle.
1998		Designed and built the Maltese Falcon.	
1999 Decide to write Autobiography.		The Maltese Falcon runs.	

WHAT THEY SAY:
Foreign Views

THE MINIMAG MAGNETO

Without a doubt, the best miniature magneto that is commercially produced is the MINIMAG produced by Jim Shelley of Walsall, England. An outline view of the basic design is shown.

From Strictly IC Magazine. Bob Shores
Ruskin, Florida.
U.S.A.

THE CRANKSHAFT THAT GREW

Jim Shelley of MINIMAG fame has, for years, manufactured magnetos for model engines with a front end replacement unit comprising magneto, crankshaft, and front housing for engines having a removable front end. These units are no longer made but the magneto, as a model engineers kit, is now available with all the other accoutrements worn by spark ignition engines. I think Jim felt there was a gap in his work not making crankshafts so he jumped back on the lathe and gave way to his needs. Trouble is, he couldn't stop. After cleaning away the dust and shavings he had this massive engine – complete – on his bench. This monster is a four cylinder opposed side valve four-stroke that's only 300mm across the heads, has a capacity of 260cc and it spins a 36" prop at scale rpm. Jim has named it the 'MALTESE FALCON'. Yes, it is magneto ignition, you can build one with a small lathe, and you can purchase the bits how you please with the drawings, castings, valves, crankshaft and so on available as separate items. Best way to see it is on video, available from Jim, for £8.00. Catch 'the Limey Bastard' (his words!) while he is still up to his waste in metal shavings on 01922 628553.

Jim Shelley's 260cc Maltese Falcon – 'impressive is not the word' -Wizard of Oz.

By kind permission of RCM&E Magazine, Brian Winch, Lurnea, NSW, Australia

JIM SHELLEY DOES IT AGAIN!

After reading the Wizard of Oz column he realised that many modellers have an ardent desire to build a model engine but are hampered by the lack of workshop equipment. Setting his keen mind on the problem he came up with the perfect answer- a 'Do-It-Yourself' engine project that can be done on the dining room table by any modeller who has ever filed his nails. Yes, if you have used a nail file to trim the ends of your finger nails you have the skill required to build a 'Shelley Falcon'. All you need do is visit your friendly local car wreckers and purchase a Volkswagen or Porsch engine. When you have done this send several £s to Jim and, by return

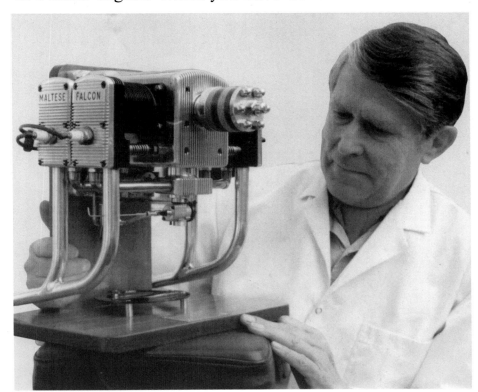

mail, he will send you a large second cut bastard file and a kit of paper templates. Stick the paper templates on the VW engine as indicated in the instruction sheet and then simply file away all the metal you can see outside the template area. In no time at all you will have re-shaped the German bug engine into a state-of-the-art British Maltese Falcon.

A little tip from the Wizard of Oz. Save all the aluminium filings in a coffee jar and, for the Yuletide season, spray your windows with contact cement and sprinkle the filings to give a nice glitter to your panes. This might just get you back into the good graces of 'her-who-must-be-obeyed' after the fuss she made about all the marks on the dining room table you caused when 'Filing your Falcon'.

Brian Winch (The Wizard of Oz), Australia

A footnote from Minimag: The views expressed on this page are not necessarily the views of the Minimag Company, who disassociate themselves with some of the technical suggestions contained therein. However, not forgetting 'There is one born every minute' the second cut bastards are now in stock.

High flier in a small world

Jim Shelley doesn't have far to walk to his workshop when he's finished his breakfast . . . it's next to his living room.

Caroline Curd meets inventor and model engineer Jim Shelley

And it's no small affair either. It boasts a lathe, milling machine, and walls of tools of every shape and size.

You might wonder why a retired salesman would need such a comprehensive set-up. Then Jim shows you the inside of his huge garage and it all starts to become clear.

There, in all their glory, stand stunningly preserved vintage cars and motorbikes, ranging from a 1927 Alvis 'Ducksback' to a 1933 Lagonda tourer.

And there's more. He opens the door into his spare bedroom and reveals a virtual showroom of model planes of all shapes and sizes, some suspended from the ceiling; others neatly lined up on special shelving.

I'm at his home in Walsall because of another of his passions – building and flying model aircraft – and already I am amazed at this talented man's capacity to pack every hour with his hobbies.

"The only reason I found time to fit it all in is because I didn't get married," confides the softly-spoken Jim.

"No one, if they were married, would be able to have a workshop at the end of the lounge without a bit of conflict!"

As an antidote to his hours at the workbench, he plays in his own band, the Jim Shelley Frisco Jazz Band, but that's yet another story!

Jim's early career was in engineering, and his inspiration for creating model engines and aeroplanes was sparked by renowned Midlands engineer the late Gerald Smith who, among many other things, designed the undercarriage for Hurricanes and Lancaster bombers.

"He showed me the wonderful range of model engines he had designed and built – Redwings, Lapwings, Magpies and Wizards, as well as his fabulous twin row 18

On go the wings of the Taylorcraft. It weighs 90lbs and initially Jim ran it using a lawnmower engine.

cylinder radial which won the Model Engineer Exhibition Cup in 1930," he says with a gleam in his eye.

Since then, Jim has won over 50 trophies with various model aeroplanes, and is also the proud owner of Britain's first large model aircraft which he discovered sitting in a garage showroom in Wolverhampton. This monster, the Taylorcraft, has a 15-foot wing span, and was built in 1962 by Lou Watson and powered by a 49cc engine.

Jim bought it in 1968 and rebuilt it, fitting an 85cc lawnmower engine, later to be replaced by a 100cc Flymo-type engine and a more sophisticated set of radio controls.

It has since proved a great success at shows all over the country where it tows banners, and the plane has even appeared on the BBC.

When he decided it needed extra power, Jim set about designing and building a flat four engine of 260cc

Left: Jim's immaculate Austin 7 and right, his Alvis 'Ducksback', both of which he rebuilt and restored to their original glory.

capacity based on the full-size Lycoming. He christened his baby The Maltese Falcon and says: "The satisfying and most exciting thing I have experienced was when the engine ran properly for the first time back in April this year."

He is happy to pass on his expertise to other modellers, and sells videos and engineering drawings of the Maltese Falcon.

Jim's other major achievement is his invention of the Minimag Miniature Magneto, a miniature magnet which creates the spark to run an engine. He now sells kits to modellers all over the world since launching it in the mid-80s.

"We've had some fantastic fun with the models over the years," laughs Jim, who admits to once knocking down a fence at Shugborough Hall, home of the Earl of Lichfield, when the Taylorcraft over-shot a landing.

"Of all the shows, the one that sticks in my mind was a game fair at Weston Hall, in Staffordshire, where I was booked to fly a banner saying 'Welcome Subaru owners'.

"The only place from which to take off was a lawn in front of the hall.

"The hall was dead ahead of me and each side of it were poplar trees taller than the house. I only had a 100cc engine and the wind had dropped.

"I put the full power on, revved it a couple of times and it took off, heading directly towards the upstairs windows. I thought 'it's never going to get over the hall with this big banner on', but it managed to miss the roof by 15 feet!"

ITEMS AVAILABLE

MINIMAG CO

- Boxed Engineer's Magneto Kit (see brochure).
  - (includes 'SPARK DEMON' and building instructions).
- Rotor only ALCOMAX IV.
  - Ground to 1.007 inch O.D. and 0.317 inch I.D. magnetised.
- The new 'SPARK DEMON'.
- Higher 2.5 Volts to 6 Volts. Lightweight H.T. capacitor unit on 0.375 Inch square. lamination stack. Weight 100 Grams.
- Standard 'MINIMAG' quarter inch spark plug ALUMINA Insulator 32 TPI X 3.00 inch reach.
- K.L.G. short reach quarter inch spark plug 32 TPI X 0.15 inch reach.
- Plug Adaptor (quarter inch to three eighths by 24 TPI).

MALTESE FALCON.
- Construction Video.
- Half size engineering drawings (11 sheets of A3).
- Step by step construction book (40 Photographs on 40 pages).
- Crankcase and Crankshaft castings.

- Free brochure and Price List from: Minimag Co.
  358, Birmingham Road.
  Walsall. WS5 3NX

FRISCO JAZZ.
For Bookings, current CD's, Cassettes and Discography, contact above address
or Phone 01922 628553

ACKNOWLEDGEMENTS

This morning whilst lifting my silver tea-spoon to crack open my boiled egg, my eyes focused on the inscription WGC on the handle and it made me realise I had been very lucky. I had been fortunate to have been sent to Public school, apprenticed at Walsall Pressings and learned 'life' at Columbus Dixon. *My eggs were not all in one basket.* My father Jack Shelley, had won the spoon, obviously in a competition at Walsall Golf Club, of which he had been the Captain. It was no longer in a case, but serving a useful function in my cutlery drawer.

I was reminded of a conversation with Gordon Whitworth, a trumpet player with my band, who said, " It's alright for you Jim, you were born with a silver spoon in your mouth", indicating that I did not have to play Jazz in order to make ends meet. Whilst this was true to some extent, I pointed out that unlike most musicians, *I was up and at* it at 6.30 am in my workshop, engrossed in making Magnetos, Sparkplugs, an Engine or maybe rebuilding a Lagonda water-pump. With my Black Country background and on-the-job training, plus a Lathe and Miller, this was second nature to me.

I had inadvertently learned so much from meeting and befriending some of the best engineers in the world. Yes! I had been born with a silver spoon, waiting to be picked up, so I grabbed it.

The most gratifying aspect of compiling this book has been the generous response of not only the people included, who are still living, but also the many friends and relatives of those now deceased.

My sincere thanks to all who have sent rare photographs and memories and taken time to talk to me remembering the past. It should be pointed out that it is a characteristic of Midlands and Black Country people, especially engineers and designers, to be extremely reluctant to boast of their achievements. Some of the photos had to be taken clandestinely and triumphs extracted painfully like teeth. **N.B**. I do not include Carl Chinn or myself in this category otherwise this book would never have been written – but somebody's got to do it.

A touch of magic:

Special thanks to brother Tony for typing the entire draft and fellow magician Eric Moorfield, for technical know-how and computer work, also Bryan Atherton and Stan Hill for proof-reading.
I would like to thank my pal Jim Martin who personifies the quiet genius and is responsible for all electrical work on all the projects in this book. 'Silent' Jim is the electrical equivalent of the genie of Aladdin's lamp without the smoke (see article on Electrical Theory).
Never has so much been achieved and so little said about it by any group within the confines of such a small geographical location in the world than that who form the marvellous magic of the Midlands and Black Country.
I thank them all and of course my mother and father, for the foresight of having me in the correct location at the right time.